From fleece to fabric

GW00400299

National Museum Wales Books

First published in 2009 by National Museum Wales Books, Cathays Park, Cardiff, CF10 3NP, Wales.

© National Museum of Wales

ISBN 978-0-7200-0602-5

Text: Peter Gill & Associates, Ann Whittall
Design: Peter Gill & Associates
Editor: Mari Gordon
Also available in Welsh as
O ddafad i ddefnydd,
ISBN 978-0-7200-0603-2

Sponsored by
Welsh Assembly Government

Contents

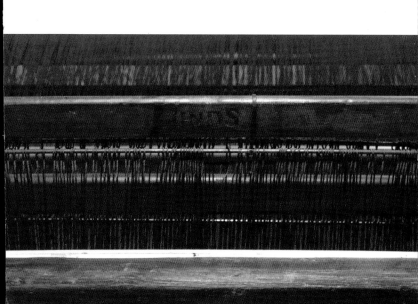

The woollen industry in Wales

The skill of weaving woollen cloth dates back to prehistoric times, and down through the centuries it has been one of Wales's most important industries. In the Middle Ages woollen manufacturing was particularly important in the county of Pembroke, where natives and Flemish immigrants spun yarn and wove cloth in their cottages and farmhouses. At that time manufacturing cloth was little more than a domestic pursuit, and the people of west Wales worked the wool of local sheep to provide themselves with blankets and rugs, tweeds and flannel.

By the end of the sixteenth century the demand for Welsh cloth had fallen away to such an extent that the industry almost disappeared from south-west Wales. But as the industry in that area declined, it caught on rapidly in the old counties of Montgomery, Merioneth and south Denbigh. A canal was constructed in 1821 to take flannel to England, allowing cargo to be sent directly from Newtown to Manchester.

Montgomeryshire could have developed into one of the most important textile manufacturing districts in Britain if the roads, railways and canals around it had not led eastwards into the heart of the Lancashire textile industry.

Sheep shearing, near Dolgellau in Gwynedd.

If coal supplies had been nearer, Newtown could truly have lived up to its name of 'the Leeds of Wales'. As it was, the manufacturers of Montgomeryshire made a serious mistake when power looms became common. They tried to compete with the textile manufacturers of northern England by building huge, steam-driven mills that produced flannel similar to that fashioned by the looms of Rochdale and Huddersfield. By 1860 the industry was in difficulty – bankruptcy and unemployment were rife. By the end of the nineteenth century the woollen industry was almost dead, and Newtown went back to being a small market town.

A water-powered wheel.

Welsh wool featured heavily in the 'traditional' Welsh costume encouraged by Lady Llanover in the early 19th century. She wanted to support the woollen industry, which was by then in decline.

The world's first ever mail-order business was established at Newtown by Pryce Jones's Royal Welsh Warehouse. His catalogue of 1887 notes that he supplied 'Real Welsh Flannel direct from the looms, Gentlemen's Welsh Tweeds, Shawls, Blankets, Hosiery and sterling value clothing for the poor'. The front cover of the catalogue shows that he supplied the Royal Family and the Crowned Heads of Europe.

The Pryce Jones Royal Welsh Warehouse in Newtown.

The woollen industry in the Teifi Valley

As the industry declined in mid and north Wales, the Teifi Valley in west Wales became the new heart of the nation's woollen industry. By 1895 the three counties of Dyfed – Cardiganshire, Carmarthenshire and Pembrokeshire – boasted as many as 325 woollen mills. Life in villages such as Dre-fach Felindre, Pentre-cwrt and Llandysul revolved around the factory and the production of flannel shirts, underwear and blankets for the ever-growing industrial districts of

south Wales. By 1900, the Dre-fach Felindre area was home to 52 mills in full production. Between 1890 and 1920 there was a constant demand for the fruit of these looms, and fortunes were made by the mill owners who could call on an adequate supply of labour. Many village children would work from 5pm to 8pm on school days for three pence and from 8am to 1pm on Saturdays for four pence.

Families and neighbours gathered together for the shearing.

Far left: A handloom and a twisting wheel at Frondeg Mill.
Left: A carding engine.

'There are no parishes in Wales that produce more Welsh flannel'

Dre-fach Felindre was a true industrial village and its whole life was tied up with the process of textile manufacture. Almost all the people of the village, dubbed the 'Huddersfield of Wales', were concerned with some aspect of the process. Most worked in the local mills, while others weaved in their own homes. Many were engaged as outworkers making up shirts, shawls and underwear for one or other of the mills.

In 1897 a local historian wrote:

There are no parishes in Wales that produce more Welsh flannel … Nearly all the power of the streams and rivers has been harnessed to drive machines. There is hardly a spot on the banks of rivers where it would be convenient to build an additional factory or mill.

Dre-fach Felindre's success as a major wool manufacturing area was down to three main factors. Firstly, the swiftly flowing waters of the Bargod, Esgair and Brân streams provided the water to drive machinery and to wash and scour raw wool and fabrics. Secondly, wool was in plentiful supply as the village was surrounded by sheep farms, and the area had a long tradition of hand-loom weaving, spinning yarn and stocking knitting before the development of factories. Finally, when the railway reached Pencader in 1864 and Newcastle Emlyn in 1895 it provided the means of taking the produce of the industry to its main market in the industrial valleys of south Wales.

Washing sheep in the traditional way, using coracles, in Cenarth.

The two World Wars made huge fortunes for the mills as fabric was needed to clothe millions of soldiers. However, after the Second World War, the price of wool plummeted and the mills began to close down. The 1960s saw a mini-boom when the mills of the Teifi Valley produced tapestry cloth as fashion designers such as Mary Quant became very interested in using it. However this was short-lived. In 1976, Cambrian Mills became the home of the National Wool Museum.

Above: Cambrian Mills at work, in 1961.
Right: the Butterworth & Dickinson loom. Welsh red flannel was believed to have healing properties.

James Lewis ('James the clerk') sorting fleece at Cambrian Mills.

The process – from fleece to fabric

Shearing

Sheep are traditionally shorn in the early summer before the weather gets too hot and they begin to shed their wool naturally. Shearing was the social highlight of the year on the remote mountain farms. Groups of neighbours would gather at each farm. Children would catch the sheep for the men to shear by hand, while the women prepared special shearing teas. Most Welsh farms now employ groups of skilled travelling shearers, many of them from Australia and New Zealand.

Farmers often washed the sheep beforehand in a *pwll* (sheep's pool). If the sheep had been washed before shearing, the farmers were paid more for the fleece.

Sorting

Wool varies tremendously from sheep breed to sheep breed, but there are also variations in different sections of a fleece. The better quality wool from the shoulders and sides has to be separated from the short, often dirty wool of the tail, belly and legs.

If a fleece were used without sorting, the resulting yarn would be faulty and uneven, and dyeing would be patchy.

The wool used at Cambrian Mills came mainly from New Zealand and Australia. Women usually sorted the wool at Cambrian Mills. They worked in the large attic areas, sorting the fleeces into different containers.

The mill buildings at the Museum are full of original graffiti. When they thought they wouldn't be seen by the manager, and to pass the time, the women wrote or carved messages on the timber beams. Here's one of the messages you can still see at the Museum:

*Think of me when you
are happy
Keep for me a tender spot
In the depth of your affection
Plant a sweet forget me not*

Dyeing

Before the invention of synthetic dyes, textile workers throughout the world depended on natural dyes. Lichens, red currants, bracken, onion skins, heather, gorse and hundreds of other plants were used to produce different colours. Chemical dyes were invented in 1856, and they were cheaper, easier to produce and guaranteed uniformity of colour. Wool was dyed at Cambrian Mills in large vats filled with boiling water and chemical dyes. The waste water from the dyeing and washing process was emptied straight into the river, which would run yellow-blue because of the dyes.

Bitten by the devil

A willowing machine is also called a willeyer, teaser, *chwalwr, diawl, diafol* or 'The Devil' because of its sharp teeth – a worker at Ffatri Tŷ Main Mill had his arm ripped off by this machine.

Willowing

Also known as 'willying', this is the process of disentangling fleece wool and getting rid of impurities such as dust and sand. For the last 150 years or so, willying has been a mechanical process, using a power-driven machine that resembles a barn thresher.

The willy, or 'devil', with its large revolving drum covered with rows of iron spikes opens up the wool in preparation for 'carding', creating a soft, fluffy mass of fibres. The machine at the Museum is electrically powered and originally came from Derw Mills in Pentre-cwrt. There were two willowers at Cambrian Mills, so that undyed and dyed wool could be willowed separately. This stopped the different coloured fibres from getting mixed up.

The carding engine.

Carding

Carding is the process of opening out the fibres of wool to produce a disentangled, soft roll of wool ready for spinning into yarn. According to the most proficient weavers, the key to the quality of cloth is the nature of the yarn, and this itself depends on the process of carding. According to one local mill owner, the carding engine was 'The temple of the mill', because if the carding equipment is in poor condition the efforts of the spinner and weaver would all be in vain. In Wales, the earliest method of carding was to place prickly teasel heads in a rectangular hand frame; a pair of frames was then used to produce disentangled 'rovings'. So important was the teasel plant in the industry that its name in Welsh is *Llysiau'r Cribwr* ('the carder's plant').

A carding machine has a series of revolving rollers covered with card brushing. The carding engine at the Museum consists of two machines: the scribbler, responsible for the initial disentangling of wool, and the carder itself, with fine brushing for producing continuous rolls or 'slivers' of wool. Cambrian Mills had four carding machines, 20 metres long and weighing 10 tons each. The carding engine you see today has come from Abbey Woollen Mill and is representative of the type that would have been in use at Cambrian Mills.

Taking the 'p'!

In most of the mills of Wales, wool was processed without any preliminary washing or scouring, but in a few of the larger mills, such as Cambrian Mills, wool was scoured before willowing. The most common method of scouring was to immerse raw wool in a solution consisting of one part human urine to three parts water. The practice of collecting urine in a cask from people's homes was common in Dre-fach Felindre until the 1930s. Urine was also important in the dyeing and finishing of the cloth.

Spinning

Carded rolls are soft, thick and easily broken. They can't be used for weaving until they are made stronger by stretching and twisting, and this is the process of spinning. The early method of spinning yarn was with a spindle and whorl; archaeologists have found examples of these at Iron Age sites all over Britain. By the fourteenth century the Great Wheel, also known as the Walking Wheel, was devised and this piece of equipment remained in use in Wales as a domestic process until the end of the nineteenth century. Many women of the Teifi Valley produced the yarn demanded by the handloom weavers and stocking knitters of the area. The invention of a spinning mule in the

The spinning mule.

eighteenth century revolutionised this process. A spinning wheel is operated by one person and produces one thread, while a spinning mule is operated by one person but produces hundreds of threads simultaneously. The hand spinners of west Wales objected violently to the introduction of such labour saving devices, but most of the mills in the Dre-fach Felindre area had bought them by the end of the nineteenth century, with the result that most of the spinners were deprived of their livelihood.

A spinster's tale
Throughout the centuries, spinning has been regarded exclusively as women's work – hence the word 'spinster'.

Winding and warping

Winding, unwinding and winding on again are all essential processes in preparing the yarn for weaving. Yarns from a spinning mule have to be wound on spools or cones to make the 'warp' of cloth (the long threads that go lengthways across the cloth). Warping is one of the most intricate of all textile processes; all the threads have to be placed in the correct order with the correct colour sequence before weaving can proceed. The finished warp has to be transferred to the loom and each individual thread tied by hand into the hundreds of 'heddles', the vertical wire or linen threads on the loom.

To produce the 'weft' (the threads that run widthways) wool has to be wound on shorter pieces of wood or metal, known as 'pirns' or 'bobbins', that can fit into the flying shuttle of a loom.

Tying the knot

To tie the warp onto the 90-inch Dobcross Loom at Cambrian Mills involves tying 2,000 threads by hand!

Left: Using the spinning mule.
Above: Cones of yarn at Cambrian Mills.

33

Weaving

Weaving is the process of interlacing the threads of the weft between the threads of the warp. The warp is inserted first and the weft is completed by passing a shuttle that carries the thread in between the warp threads. The threads of the warp have to be opened to provide a space, or 'shed', for the shuttle to travel through. As a length of cloth is completed it is beaten to make it firm and compact. This process is exactly the same whether it's a medieval warp-weighted loom or a twentieth-century electrically driven power loom. By the late fourteenth century, the hand loom with its pedals had taken over from the warp-weighted loom, and it was this device that was to dominate cloth production in Wales until the adoption of the power loom in the late nineteenth century. The looms at the Museum were commonplace in west Wales. These range from the wide blanket loom to the small Butterworth & Dickinson cloth looms that became particularly popular in the mills of the Teifi valley for the production of narrow-width flannel.

The Dobcross was the most popular loom of the 20th century. It produced wide cloth, and so was perfect for weaving shawls and blankets. One man could operate two of these looms at a time. Using both looms, in five days he could produce around 450 yards of cloth!

The Hattersley Pedal Loom.

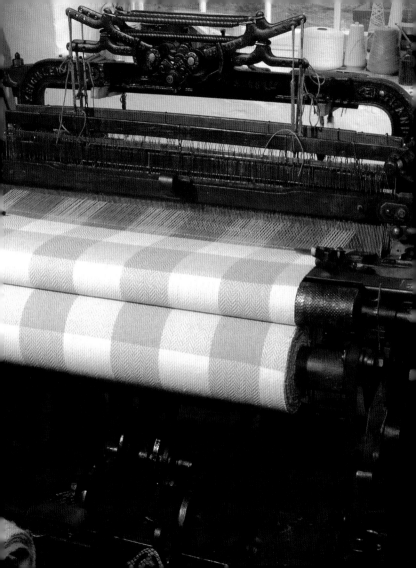

Fulling

Fulling is the process of shrinking and thickening the cloth after weaving. In the Middle Ages, this was done by placing a length of cloth in a stream and walking over it with bare feet. In the fourteenth century, water-driven mills consisting of heavy hammers that beat the cloth became commonplace in Wales and fulling became the first process to be carried out in a mill building rather than in the home. With the addition of fuller's earth, human urine and a great deal of water, woven cloth was shrunk and thickened. Light flannels and the lighter variety of tweeds produced by Welsh mills did not need this heavy fulling process; it was enough to wash cloth and mill it in scouring machines using soda and soap flakes. These milling machines can be seen in the Wash Room at the Museum together with an Open Width Scourer that is still used to wash blankets and an industrial spin drier known as the Hydro.

Welsh place names that include 'pandy', such as Tonypandy, indicate the position of early fulling mills.

A completed traditional Cambrian Mills Doublecloth Tapestry.

Cambrian
Mills
LLANDYSSUL
woven by Welsh craftsmen

PURE NEW *wool*

Drying

After washing, damp woollen cloth was stretched into shape on a tenter frame with tenter hooks, and left to dry outside or in wind sheds which were used to protect the drying fabrics from rain and sunshine.

At Cambrian Mills the Tenter Machine dried cloth under tension as it passed over a series of steam-heated pipes. It could dry 72 yards of cloth at a time in less than half an hour. The Tenter Box, which looks like a blue hut built around the machine, held the heat inside.

Finishing

Different finishes, such as fluffy, smooth or pressed are applied to woollen fabrics depending on their purpose. Traditional nursing shawls were pressed between cardboard sheets in a seven-shawl sandwich in a hot press, followed by a period under pressure in a cold press. This was to ensure that the finished shawl had a smooth, pressed surface that would not irritate a baby's skin.

Nature meets machine

Teasels were traditionally used to 'comb' the surface of dry woollen cloth by hand to make it soft and fluffy. This is called 'raising the nap'. A machine called the Teasel Gig was invented to make this process faster and more efficient. It contained around 3,000 prickly teasels in an iron frame and the cloth was passed over the teasels to give it a more even, fluffy finish. This machine was then replaced by a fully mechanised version – the Moser Raiser, which can be seen in operation at the Museum.

The teasel plant, known in Welsh as *Llysiau'r Cribwr* – 'the carder's plant'.

Wool

Wool is the most versatile textile fibre known to man. From its unique properties, Welsh woollen mills have produced many materials and products, from working clothes and fine furnishing fabrics to tourist souvenirs.

Early Welsh blankets often featured bold, vertical stripes in black, navy or brown on a natural cream background. Plaids were also immensely popular and, during the nineteenth century, also featured strong, dark colours against a cream background. Later blankets tended to incorporate more colours and there was a predilection for pastel shades. Traditional shawls were hugely popular with tourists visiting Wales in the 1950s and 1960s. The Cambrian Mills nursing shawls were often woven in pink, blue and fawn checked pattern.

The Museum's Textile Gallery showcases the wide variety of historic textiles that were created throughout Wales. The gallery highlights the tradition and importance of woollen textiles in Welsh life, from the nursing shawls that we wrapped our babies in, to the flannel shirts that were worn by working men and the bold stripes and checks of the traditional Welsh costume. The gallery's Wall of Blankets, made up from a variety of different types of blankets – check, striped and tapestry – strikes a chord with many of our visitors, as they remember similar blankets from their own homes. The collection continues to grow: the latest addition has been a collection of clothes made in the 1960s and 1970s from fabric purchased at Cambrian Mills.

Traditional style Welsh shawls.

The National Wool Museum

The Museum is housed in the original Cambrian Mills buildings, which have all been sympathetically restored. Original machinery has been restored to working condition, and the gallery displays a collection of blankets, shawls and quilts. From a raised walkway visitors can enjoy a unique view of a contemporary commercial weaver working on traditional textiles.

Guided tours and demonstrations of the machinery offer an insight into this traditional Welsh industry.

The Museum shop sells a wide range of contemporary woven textiles and the café serves fresh food sourced from local producers.

A wide range of activities are available. Please contact the Museum on (01559) 370929 for further information or to arrange group visits.

national wool museum amgueddfa wlân cymru

Wales's national museums

Amgueddfa Cymru is a family of seven museums located throughout Wales. Each family member gives a unique and vivid experience of Wales's history, while sharing the Amgueddfa Cymru values of excellence and learning.

The National Wool Museum
Dre-fach Felindre, Carmarthenshire

The National Waterfront Museum
Maritime Quarter, Swansea

National Museum Cardiff
Cathays Park, Cardiff

St Fagans: National History Museum
St Fagans, Cardiff

Big Pit: National Coal Museum
Blaenafon, Torfaen

The National Slate Museum
Llanberis, Gwynedd

The National Roman Legion Museum
Caerleon, Newport

Find out more about the 'hidden' collections on our website Rhagor – www.museumwales.ac.uk/Rhagor.